MATH FACT FLUENCY & MORE

Ollie B. Wheeler   Edwin S. Oliver

Hi, I am Caleb. My friends and I created this book to help you with your math fact fluency. We believe that fact fluency is key to success in math. If you want to become a math whiz, you should practice your math skills daily. This book begins by teaching you basic concepts that build on each other and get more difficult as you go. Have fun working through this book. There's no pressure—take your time and enjoy.

Hana   Gracie   Diego

THIS BOOK BELONGS TO

_____

_____

_____

I AM
OLLIE!
CHILDREN'S BOOKS

POSITIVE MATH AFFIRMATIONS

- I am excited about math.

- I enjoy solving math problems.

- I am a mathematician.

- I am a tree spouting with knowledge.

- I love learning math in new ways.

- I can successfully work through challenging math problems.

- I am a resilient problem solver.

- My mistakes are opportunities to grow and learn.

- I am determined to always excel at math.

- I am a scholar—a whiz who has overcome my math fears.

ADDING ZERO

$$\begin{array}{r} 3 \\ + 0 \\ \hline \end{array} \qquad \begin{array}{r} 6 \\ + 0 \\ \hline \end{array} \qquad \begin{array}{r} 4 \\ + 0 \\ \hline \end{array} \qquad \begin{array}{r} 0 \\ + 5 \\ \hline \end{array}$$

$$\begin{array}{r} 7 \\ + 0 \\ \hline \end{array} \qquad \begin{array}{r} 2 \\ + 0 \\ \hline \end{array} \qquad \begin{array}{r} 8 \\ + 0 \\ \hline \end{array} \qquad \begin{array}{r} 0 \\ + 9 \\ \hline \end{array}$$

$$\begin{array}{r} 0 \\ + 0 \\ \hline \end{array} \qquad \begin{array}{r} 1 \\ + 0 \\ \hline \end{array} \qquad \begin{array}{r} 0 \\ + 6 \\ \hline \end{array} \qquad \begin{array}{r} 0 \\ + 4 \\ \hline \end{array}$$

$$\begin{array}{r} 0 \\ + 3 \\ \hline \end{array} \qquad \begin{array}{r} 5 \\ + 0 \\ \hline \end{array} \qquad \begin{array}{r} 9 \\ + 0 \\ \hline \end{array} \qquad \begin{array}{r} 0 \\ + 7 \\ \hline \end{array}$$

add, altogether, all, in all, increase, increased by, more than, together, sum, total, total number

ADDING ZERO

5 + 0	0 + 3	6 + 0	0 + 2
9 + 0	7 + 0	0 + 8	0 + 1
0 + 6	10 + 0	0 + 5	0 + 7
4 + 0	8 + 0	1 + 0	3 + 0

4

ADDING ONE

$$\begin{array}{r} 6 \\ +\ 1 \\ \hline \end{array}\qquad\begin{array}{r} 1 \\ +\ 3 \\ \hline \end{array}\qquad\begin{array}{r} 8 \\ +\ 1 \\ \hline \end{array}\qquad\begin{array}{r} 2 \\ +\ 1 \\ \hline \end{array}$$

$$\begin{array}{r} 5 \\ +\ 1 \\ \hline \end{array}\qquad\begin{array}{r} 1 \\ +\ 7 \\ \hline \end{array}\qquad\begin{array}{r} 9 \\ +\ 1 \\ \hline \end{array}\qquad\begin{array}{r} 4 \\ +\ 1 \\ \hline \end{array}$$

$$\begin{array}{r} 0 \\ +\ 1 \\ \hline \end{array}\qquad\begin{array}{r} 1 \\ +\ 3 \\ \hline \end{array}\qquad\begin{array}{r} 1 \\ +\ 5 \\ \hline \end{array}\qquad\begin{array}{r} 1 \\ +\ 1 \\ \hline \end{array}$$

$$\begin{array}{r} 1 \\ +\ 4 \\ \hline \end{array}\qquad\begin{array}{r} 1 \\ +\ 6 \\ \hline \end{array}\qquad\begin{array}{r} 1 \\ +\ 8 \\ \hline \end{array}\qquad\begin{array}{r} 3 \\ +\ 1 \\ \hline \end{array}$$

ADDING ONE

7 + 1	1 + 5	6 + 1	1 + 3
4 + 1	8 + 1	1 + 0	2 + 1
9 + 1	1 + 4	1 + 2	5 + 1
3 + 1	1 + 7	1 + 6	0 + 1

ADDING 2 AND 3

8	2	3	6
+ 2	+ 4	+ 5	+ 3

7	4	1	5
+ 3	+ 3	+ 2	+ 2

6	5	1	4
+ 2	+ 4	+ 3	+ 2

2	0	2	7
+ 8	+ 3	+ 6	+ 2

ADDING 2 AND 3

6	3	7	5
+ 2	+ 8	+ 2	+ 3

9	1	8	4
+ 2	+ 3	+ 3	+ 2

3	3	3	0
+ 6	+ 9	+ 4	+ 2

2	4	2	7
+ 3	+ 3	+ 9	+ 3

ADDING 5

5	4	5	5
+ 3	+ 5	+ 5	+ 9

2	5	7	5
+ 5	+ 6	+ 5	+ 0

1	9	5	3
+ 5	+ 5	+ 8	+ 5

5	0	5	5
+ 7	+ 5	+ 2	+ 1

ADDING 5

$$
\begin{array}{r} 5 \\ +6 \\ \hline \end{array}
\qquad
\begin{array}{r} 7 \\ +5 \\ \hline \end{array}
\qquad
\begin{array}{r} 5 \\ +4 \\ \hline \end{array}
\qquad
\begin{array}{r} 3 \\ +5 \\ \hline \end{array}
$$

$$
\begin{array}{r} 5 \\ +1 \\ \hline \end{array}
\qquad
\begin{array}{r} 8 \\ +5 \\ \hline \end{array}
\qquad
\begin{array}{r} 2 \\ +5 \\ \hline \end{array}
\qquad
\begin{array}{r} 9 \\ +5 \\ \hline \end{array}
$$

$$
\begin{array}{r} 4 \\ +5 \\ \hline \end{array}
\qquad
\begin{array}{r} 0 \\ +5 \\ \hline \end{array}
\qquad
\begin{array}{r} 5 \\ +8 \\ \hline \end{array}
\qquad
\begin{array}{r} 6 \\ +5 \\ \hline \end{array}
$$

$$
\begin{array}{r} 5 \\ +5 \\ \hline \end{array}
\qquad
\begin{array}{r} 5 \\ +7 \\ \hline \end{array}
\qquad
\begin{array}{r} 1 \\ +5 \\ \hline \end{array}
\qquad
\begin{array}{r} 5 \\ +9 \\ \hline \end{array}
$$

ADDING 6 AND 7

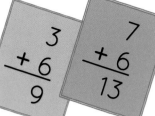

$$\begin{array}{r} 3 \\ +\ 6 \\ \hline 9 \end{array} \qquad \begin{array}{r} 7 \\ +\ 6 \\ \hline 13 \end{array}$$

$$\begin{array}{r} 2 \\ +\ 6 \\ \hline \end{array} \qquad \begin{array}{r} 8 \\ +\ 6 \\ \hline \end{array} \qquad \begin{array}{r} 9 \\ +\ 7 \\ \hline \end{array} \qquad \begin{array}{r} 7 \\ +\ 7 \\ \hline \end{array}$$

$$\begin{array}{r} 6 \\ +\ 7 \\ \hline \end{array} \qquad \begin{array}{r} 6 \\ +\ 4 \\ \hline \end{array} \qquad \begin{array}{r} 5 \\ +\ 6 \\ \hline \end{array} \qquad \begin{array}{r} 7 \\ +\ 3 \\ \hline \end{array}$$

$$\begin{array}{r} 0 \\ +\ 6 \\ \hline \end{array} \qquad \begin{array}{r} 6 \\ +\ 6 \\ \hline \end{array} \qquad \begin{array}{r} 1 \\ +\ 7 \\ \hline \end{array} \qquad \begin{array}{r} 9 \\ +\ 6 \\ \hline \end{array}$$

$$\begin{array}{r} 7 \\ +\ 2 \\ \hline \end{array} \qquad \begin{array}{r} 4 \\ +\ 7 \\ \hline \end{array} \qquad \begin{array}{r} 8 \\ +\ 7 \\ \hline \end{array} \qquad \begin{array}{r} 3 \\ +\ 6 \\ \hline \end{array}$$

ADDING 8 AND 9

$$8 + 5 \qquad 4 + 8 \qquad 9 + 2 \qquad 4 + 9$$

$$9 + 8 \qquad 8 + 4 \qquad 7 + 8 \qquad 6 + 9$$

$$1 + 9 \qquad 9 + 0 \qquad 6 + 8 \qquad 9 + 6$$

$$8 + 2 \qquad 9 + 7 \qquad 8 + 7 \qquad 3 + 8$$

DOUBLES

6	2	5	8
+ 6	+ 2	+ 5	+ 8

0	3	7	4
+ 0	+ 3	+ 7	+ 4

1	9	6	5
+ 1	+ 9	+ 6	+ 5

8	7	4	9
+ 8	+ 7	+ 4	+ 9

NEAR DOUBLES

4 + 5	6 + 7	3 + 2	8 + 7
5 + 6	9 + 8	7 + 6	0 + 1
3 + 4	5 + 4	6 + 5	2 + 1
8 + 9	1 + 0	7 + 8	4 + 3

3 ADDENDS ADDITION

7	8	5	9	4	9
2	4	5	3	2	5
+ 5	+ 3	+ 2	+ 8	+ 3	+ 0

2	3	4	5	6	7
3	9	5	5	8	8
+ 2	+ 3	+ 4	+ 5	+ 6	+ 7

2	8	5	6	4	5
3	2	4	7	8	8
+ 7	+ 5	+ 6	+ 9	+ 6	+ 8

10	14	15	20	12	15
4	3	2	3	4	5
+ 4	+ 1	+ 2	+ 5	+ 4	+ 3

SUBTRACT WITH ZERO

$$\begin{array}{r} 3 \\ -\ 0 \\ \hline \end{array} \qquad \begin{array}{r} 6 \\ -\ 0 \\ \hline \end{array} \qquad \begin{array}{r} 4 \\ -\ 0 \\ \hline \end{array} \qquad \begin{array}{r} 0 \\ -\ 0 \\ \hline \end{array}$$

$$\begin{array}{r} 7 \\ -\ 7 \\ \hline \end{array} \qquad \begin{array}{r} 2 \\ -\ 0 \\ \hline \end{array} \qquad \begin{array}{r} 8 \\ -\ 8 \\ \hline \end{array} \qquad \begin{array}{r} 7 \\ -\ 0 \\ \hline \end{array}$$

$$\begin{array}{r} 3 \\ -\ 0 \\ \hline \end{array} \qquad \begin{array}{r} 5 \\ -\ 0 \\ \hline \end{array} \qquad \begin{array}{r} 9 \\ -\ 9 \\ \hline \end{array} \qquad \begin{array}{r} 1 \\ -\ 1 \\ \hline \end{array}$$

$$\begin{array}{r} 5 \\ -\ 5 \\ \hline \end{array} \qquad \begin{array}{r} 8 \\ -\ 0 \\ \hline \end{array} \qquad \begin{array}{r} 6 \\ -\ 6 \\ \hline \end{array} \qquad \begin{array}{r} 9 \\ -\ 0 \\ \hline \end{array}$$

minus, subtract, take away, greater than, fewer than, less than, decreased by

SUBTRACT 1 AND 2

9 - 1	5 - 2	4 - 1	8 - 2
6 - 2	3 - 1	7 - 2	2 - 1
2 - 2	9 - 2	5 - 1	7 - 1
4 - 2	8 - 1	6 - 1	3 - 2

SUBTRACT 2 AND 3

8	7	9	6
- 2	- 2	- 3	- 3

4	3	2	5
- 2	- 3	- 2	- 3

9	8	4	6
- 2	- 3	- 3	- 2

7	3	10	10
- 3	- 2	- 2	- 3

SUBTRACT 4 AND 5

9	6	8	4
- 4	- 5	- 5	- 4

8	5	9	7
- 4	- 5	- 5	- 4

10	7	5	6
- 4	- 5	- 4	- 4

10	12	11	12
- 5	- 4	- 4	- 5

REGROUPING (ADDITION)

Tens	Ones
[1]	
4	3
+ 2	7
7	0

Tens	Ones
[1]	
5	6
+ 3	8
9	4

Regrouping is the process of making groups of tens when adding or subtracting two or more digit numbers.

Regrouping is also another name for carrying and borrowing.

In adding two or more digit numbers, always remember to start from right to left.

Tens	Ones
[1]	
7	2
+ 1	8
9	0

Tens	Ones
[1]	
4	5
+ 2	9
7	4

ADDITION

12	17	15	13	16	22	24
+ 9	+ 5	+ 7	+ 8	+ 6	+ 9	+ 8

35	36	54	47	46	57	62
+ 7	+ 6	+ 8	+ 5	+ 4	+ 8	+ 9

28	74	82	69	95	91	78
+ 88	+ 29	+ 48	+ 57	+ 46	+ 39	+ 83

45	52	85	77	68	34	87
+ 77	+ 39	+ 48	+ 54	+ 46	+ 27	+ 55

65	82	75	68	98	39	88
34	74	14	23	17	54	27
+ 36	+ 38	+ 46	+ 29	+ 49	+ 25	+ 58

MORE ADDITION

128 + 51	245 + 23	187 + 12	905 + 83	224 + 62	470 + 24
208 + 63	725 + 39	619 + 25	873 + 19	475 + 18	533 + 47
459 + 75	687 + 49	382 + 38	565 + 57	923 + 77	241 + 89
829 + 76	782 + 58	478 + 49	892 + 79	448 + 67	288 + 36
165 23 + 36	387 34 + 28	548 52 + 41	792 45 + 36	489 62 + 43	623 29 + 48
259 180 + 48	483 256 + 75	309 253 + 28	527 332 + 48	350 423 +139	457 209 +283

REGROUPING (SUBTRACTION)

Tens	Ones
3	13
4̷	3̷
- 2	7
1	6

Tens	Ones
4	16
5̷	6̷
- 3	8
1	8

☑ Subtract with regrouping when the value of the digit on the bottom is larger than the digit on top.

☑ Borrow ten from the number in the tens column.

1 ten = 10 ones

☑ Add the 10 ones to the number in the ones column.

☑ Now that the numbers on top are larger, you can now find the difference.

Tens	Ones
6	12
7̷	2̷
- 3	8
3	4

Tens	Ones
7	15
8̷	5̷
- 4	9
3	6

23

BALANCING EQUATIONS

Write the number that makes the equation true.

$12 - 5 = 5 + \boxed{}$	$20 + \boxed{} = 30 - 8$
$18 - \boxed{} = 10 + 5$	$5 + 9 = 22 - \boxed{}$
$34 - 6 = 14 + \boxed{}$	$45 + 12 = \boxed{} - 3$
$\boxed{} - 12 = 12 + 36$	$72 - 6 = 39 + \boxed{}$

SUBTRACTION

18	25	29	32	48	54	65	29
- 7	- 4	- 6	- 2	- 8	- 3	- 4	- 7

29	36	59	66	31	45	91	83
- 8	- 6	- 4	- 3	- 8	- 9	- 8	- 5

38	47	22	58	65	92	73	71
- 9	- 8	- 3	- 9	- 7	- 6	- 5	- 9

45	53	38	29	68	88	45	92
- 32	- 21	- 23	- 19	- 35	- 27	- 15	- 71

84	72	45	58	70	63	97	36
- 39	- 23	- 39	- 39	- 58	- 38	- 68	- 29

71	48	34	86	65	55	90	62
- 53	- 29	- 18	- 49	- 38	- 27	- 39	- 45

MORE SUBTRACTION

281	345	675	543	839
- 50	- 33	- 43	- 21	- 25

764	686	587	439	964
- 53	- 62	- 74	- 37	- 54

367	440	652	785	530
- 89	- 59	- 75	- 97	- 45

603	568	782	304	284
- 67	- 99	- 95	- 48	- 96

603	456	348	571	800
- 536	- 278	- 199	- 298	- 687

540	786	209	430	830
- 392	- 598	- 179	- 278	- 167

200 - 73	300 - 65	500 - 79	400 - 48
600 - 92	700 - 58	900 - 86	800 - 39
500 - 146	400 - 239	600 - 479	700 - 508
800 - 623	900 - 459	1000 - 562	2000 - 875
6000 - 987	5000 - 887	4000 - 399	3000 - 909
1000 - 745	2000 - 1448	9000 - 5789	8000 - 6883

182 - 89	280 - 93	360 - 92	742 - 59
785 - 78	689 - 98	708 - 79	589 - 98
335 - 259	623 - 469	823 - 539	733 - 498
925 - 549	776 - 399	2459 - 593	4563 - 896
5238 - 897	4750 - 899	5872 - 989	6089 - 798
3509 - 2765	2250 - 1593	4523 - 2987	6208 - 4975

Even or Odd

An even number is a number that can be divided into two equal groups.

An odd number is a number that cannot be divided into two equal groups.

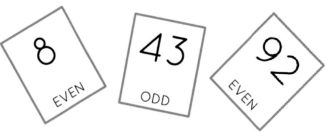

WHIZ KIDS' EXAMPLE 10	7	19	22
(Even) Odd	Even Odd	Even Odd	Even Odd
26	13	35	41
Even Odd	Even Odd	Even Odd	Even Odd
53	29	17	1
Even Odd	Even Odd	Even Odd	Even Odd
12	21	37	14
Even Odd	Even Odd	Even Odd	Even Odd

39

ODD

Even or Odd

62

EVEN

WHIZ KIDS' EXAMPLE 11 · · (stars) Even (Odd)	8 Even Odd	15 Even Odd	23 Even Odd
36 Even Odd	51 Even Odd	20 Even Odd	37 Even Odd
63 Even Odd	5 Even Odd	28 Even Odd	44 Even Odd
55 Even Odd	71 Even Odd	82 Even Odd	95 Even Odd
88 Even Odd	93 Even Odd	79 Even Odd	64 Even Odd

Even or Odd

52
EVEN

89
ODD

136	201	344	591
Even Odd	Even Odd	Even Odd	Even Odd
360	421	902	659
Even Odd	Even Odd	Even Odd	Even Odd
780	928	473	599
Even Odd	Even Odd	Even Odd	Even Odd
124	645	1,001	2,038
Even Odd	Even Odd	Even Odd	Even Odd
5,670	3,737	7,908	4,596
Even Odd	Even Odd	Even Odd	Even Odd

PATTERNS

Continue each pattern.

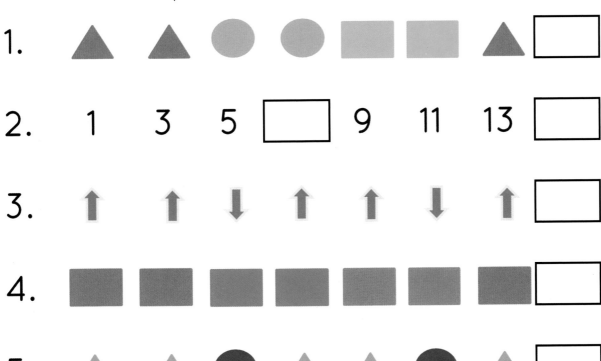

1. ▲ ▲ ● ● ▬ ▬ ▲ ☐

2. 1   3   5   ☐   9   11   13   ☐

3. ↑ ↑ ↓ ↑ ↑ ↓ ↑ ☐

4. ▬ ▬ ▬ ▬ ▬ ▬ ▬ ☐

5. ▲ ▲ ● ▲ ▲ ● ▲ ☐

Gracie created a pattern in the box below. Use the same box to create your pattern.

★★★★★★

PATTERNS

Continue each pattern.

1. A B A A B A A B ☐☐

2. 15 25 35 ☐ 55 65 75 ☐☐☐

3. ↑ ↑ → ↑ ↑ ← ↑ ☐ → ☐

4. 90 84 78 72 66 60 54 48 ☐☐

5.  ☐☐

6. 12 17 15 20 18 23 21 ☐☐☐

7. ✖ ✚ ━ ✚ ✚ ━ ✚ ✖ ✖ ☐

PATTERNS

Continue each pattern.

1. 1   5   9   [   ]   17   21   25   [   ]

2. 18   25   23   30   [   ]   35   33   [   ]

3. 60   54   48   [   ]   36   30   24   [   ]

4. 2   4   6   12   14   28   30   [   ]

5. 33   43   42   52   51   [| |]

6. 6   11   17   24   32   41   51   [   ]

7. 108   94   80   66   52   38   24   [   ]

8. 20   22   31   33   42   44   [|]

Place Value Chart

1	3	5	6
Thousands	hundreds	tens	ones

In the number 1,356
1 is in the thousands place
3 is in the hundreds place
5 is in the tens place
6 is in the ones place

How do we read this number?

Standard form	Word form	Expanded form
a way to write a number showing only its digits	a number written in words	a number written as the sum of the values of its digits
245	Two hundred forty-five	200+40+5
1,356	One thousand, three hundred fifty-six	1,000+300+50+6

Compare	Order
When you compare numbers, you determine if one number is greater than or less than another number	When you arrange numbers from least to greatest or from greatest to least
245 > 189 (245 is greater than 189) 362 < 412 (362 is less than 412)	Least to Greatest 12, 34, 48 Greatest to Least 48, 34, 12

COMPARING NUMBERS

(greater than) >, (less than) <, (equal to) =

13	<	15

23	>	21

22		12

34		37

65		56

26		62

8		08

88		80

55		50+5

12+5		19

72		70+7

12		22

90+4		48

5+20		25

33		25+8

17		12+1

36

COMPARING NUMBERS

(greater than) >, (less than) <, (equal to) =

423	<	441	<	272	>	169
545		539		539		518
387		378		392		349
909		990		90		99
629		631		631		613
817		871		822		820
9972		9970		8981		8987
555		5055		5550		5505

COMPARING NUMBERS

(greater than) >, (less than) <, (equal to) =

989	=	801 + 188
240 + 375	◯	515
777 – 200	◯	677
658	◯	240 + 320 + 18
890 – 745	◯	145
588	◯	763 – 175
1030	◯	103 + 1,000

ORDERING NUMBERS

Put the numbers in order.

Example

17, 8, 12

__8__, __12__, __17__

12, 21, 5

_____, _____, _____

23, 21, 27

_____, _____, _____

42, 49, 38

_____, _____, _____

4, 41, 14

_____, _____, _____

63, 36, 29

_____, _____, _____

72, 69, 49

_____, _____, _____

15, 61, 51

_____, _____, _____

ORDERING NUMBERS

Put the numbers in order.

203, 312, 192   521, 221, 529

_____, _____, _____   _____, _____, _____

669, 909, 901   807, 78, 708

_____, _____, _____   _____, _____, _____

1001, 988, 1011   2190, 2201, 2199

_____, _____, _____   _____, _____, _____

4590, 4890, 4499   6707, 6077, 6007

_____, _____, _____   _____, _____, _____

Place Value Tens and Ones

Fill in the number of tens and ones.

19 = _____ tens   _____ ones

34 = _____ tens   _____ ones   85 = _8_ tens _5_ ones

45 = _____ tens   _____ ones

78 = _____ tens   _____ ones   6④5

27 = _____ tens   _____ ones

63 = _____ tens   _____ ones

58 = _____ tens   _____ ones

96 = _____ tens   _____ ones

12 = _____ tens   _____ ones

80 = _____ tens   _____ ones

Circle the digit in the tens place for each number.

37   149   273   318

45

58

103   26   83   128

41

Place Value

Read the number. Look at the underlined digit. Name the place.
Write H for hundreds, T for tens, and O for ones.

2<u>3</u>0	T
<u>4</u>63	
37<u>2</u>	
<u>8</u>84	
54<u>0</u>	
<u>2</u>99	
7<u>3</u>9	
64<u>1</u>	

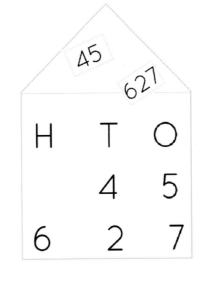

45
627

H   T   O
     4   5
6   2   7

Create the biggest and smallest numbers.

Digits	Biggest	Smallest
893	983	389
276		
439		
784		
891		
708		
329		

Place Value

Read the number. Look at the underlined digit. Name the place.
Write TH for thousands, H for hundreds, T for tens, and O for ones.
Then write the value of each underlined digit.

1,6<u>3</u>5	T	30
<u>4</u>,563		
3,7<u>9</u>5		
<u>8</u>,584		
9,6<u>2</u>8		
6,84<u>2</u>		
7,<u>5</u>54		
2,0<u>7</u>9		

Create the biggest and smallest numbers.

Digits	Biggest	Smallest
1978	9,871	1,789
2647		
6430		
5765		
3376		
8735		
2780		

Place Value

Circle each number in standard form.

One thousand, three hundred twenty-nine	1,309	Two thousand, four hundred thirty-seven	2,473
	1,392		2,437
	(1,329)		4,437
	1,029		2,137
Three thousand, forty-five	3,445	Four thousand, nine hundred twelve	4,912
	3,025		4,902
	345		4,012
	3,045		4,092
One thousand, two hundred ninety-six	1,206	Five thousand, seven hundred eleven	5,711
	2,196		5,177
	1,296		5,701
	1,996		7,511
Three thousand, six hundred thirty-eight	3,283	Two thousand, five hundred twenty-nine	2,929
	3,638		4,529
	3,683		2,509
	3,386		2,529

MULTIPLICATION/DIVISION

Multiplication	an operation that gives the total number when you join equal groups.	$3 \times 4 = 12$ number of groups · number in each group · number in all
Factors	the numbers that are multiplied together to give a product	$3 \times 4 = 12$ factor · factor
Product	the answer to a multiplication problem	$3 \times 4 = 12$ product
Division	splitting into equal parts or groups; an operation that tells how many equal groups there are or how many are in each group.	$12 \div 3 = 4$ Total · Number of equal parts · Number of each group

Multiplication and Division Fact Family		

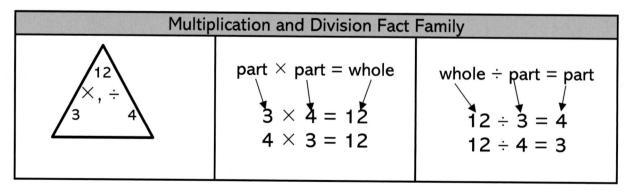

part × part = whole
$3 \times 4 = 12$
$4 \times 3 = 12$

whole ÷ part = part
$12 \div 3 = 4$
$12 \div 4 = 3$

MULTIPLY BY 0 AND 1

5 × 0	8 × 0	3 × 0	7 × 0
9 × 0	4 × 0	2 × 0	6 × 0
1 × 1	1 × 5	10 × 0	1 × 7
0 × 8	1 × 4	11 × 0	1 × 3
0 ×12	1 × 2	1 × 6	1 × 0
1 ×10	1 × 7	1 × 9	1 × 8
12 × 1	0 × 7	11 × 1	5 × 1

× product, multiply, multiplied by, times

MULTIPLY BY 2 AND 3

$$\begin{array}{r} 0 \\ \times\,2 \\ \hline \end{array} \qquad \begin{array}{r} 5 \\ \times\,2 \\ \hline \end{array} \qquad \begin{array}{r} 8 \\ \times\,2 \\ \hline \end{array} \qquad \begin{array}{r} 7 \\ \times\,2 \\ \hline \end{array}$$

$$\begin{array}{r} 2 \\ \times\,2 \\ \hline \end{array} \qquad \begin{array}{r} 4 \\ \times\,2 \\ \hline \end{array} \qquad \begin{array}{r} 6 \\ \times\,2 \\ \hline \end{array} \qquad \begin{array}{r} 10 \\ \times\,2 \\ \hline \end{array}$$

$$\begin{array}{r} 1 \\ \times\,2 \\ \hline \end{array} \qquad \begin{array}{r} 3 \\ \times\,2 \\ \hline \end{array} \qquad \begin{array}{r} 0 \\ \times\,3 \\ \hline \end{array} \qquad \begin{array}{r} 1 \\ \times\,3 \\ \hline \end{array}$$

$$\begin{array}{r} 8 \\ \times\,3 \\ \hline \end{array} \qquad \begin{array}{r} 9 \\ \times\,2 \\ \hline \end{array} \qquad \begin{array}{r} 7 \\ \times\,3 \\ \hline \end{array} \qquad \begin{array}{r} 4 \\ \times\,3 \\ \hline \end{array}$$

$$\begin{array}{r} 3 \\ \times\,3 \\ \hline \end{array} \qquad \begin{array}{r} 3 \\ \times\,2 \\ \hline \end{array} \qquad \begin{array}{r} 3 \\ \times\,9 \\ \hline \end{array} \qquad \begin{array}{r} 6 \\ \times\,3 \\ \hline \end{array}$$

$$\begin{array}{r} 3 \\ \times\,10 \\ \hline \end{array} \qquad \begin{array}{r} 3 \\ \times\,7 \\ \hline \end{array} \qquad \begin{array}{r} 5 \\ \times\,3 \\ \hline \end{array} \qquad \begin{array}{r} 3 \\ \times\,8 \\ \hline \end{array}$$

$$\begin{array}{r} 12 \\ \times\,2 \\ \hline \end{array} \qquad \begin{array}{r} 3 \\ \times\,12 \\ \hline \end{array} \qquad \begin{array}{r} 11 \\ \times\,2 \\ \hline \end{array} \qquad \begin{array}{r} 11 \\ \times\,3 \\ \hline \end{array}$$

MULTIPLY BY 4 AND 5

0	7	9	6
× 4	× 4	× 4	× 4

2	4	5	10
× 4	× 4	× 4	× 4

3	8	1	2
× 4	× 4	× 4	× 5

5	1	8	7
× 5	× 5	× 5	× 5

5	4	10	9
× 3	× 2	× 5	× 5

4	6	5	4
×10	× 5	× 9	× 5

11	12	11	4
× 4	× 5	× 5	× 12

48

MULTIPLY BY 6 AND 7

5 × 6	1 × 6	4 × 6	8 × 6
3 × 6	2 × 6	6 × 6	7 × 6
9 × 6	10 × 6	0 × 6	1 × 7
8 × 7	2 × 7	4 × 7	6 × 7
5 × 7	1 × 7	3 × 7	7 × 7
7 ×10	6 × 7	7 × 9	6 × 8
12 × 6	7 ×11	12 × 7	11 × 6

MULTIPLY BY 8 AND 9

5 × 8	4 × 8	7 × 8	3 × 8
6 × 8	8 × 8	8 × 9	10 × 8
9 × 5	9 × 4	9 × 0	8 × 1
9 × 9	10 × 9	8 × 2	9 × 3
8 × 3	1 × 8	9 × 6	2 × 9
8 ×10	9 × 7	4 × 9	9 × 5
12 × 9	8 ×12	11 × 8	9 ×11

MULTIPLY BY 10

10 × 5	10 × 3	10 × 7	10 × 6
10 × 4	10 × 1	10 × 2	10 × 8
10 × 9	10 ×10	10 × 2	5 ×10
6 ×10	8 ×10	7 ×10	9 ×10
4 ×10	3 ×10	10 × 0	2 ×10
1 ×10	0 ×10	10 × 2	10 × 8
10 × 7	10 × 0	10 × 9	10 × 4

51

MULTIPLICATION CHART

1 × 1 1	1 × 2 2	1 × 3 3	1 × 4 4	1 × 5 5	1 × 6 6	1 × 7 7	1 × 8 8	1 × 9 9	1 ×10 10
2 × 1 2	2 × 2 4	2 × 3 6	2 × 4 8	2 × 5 10	2 × 6 12	2 × 7 14	2 × 8 16	2 × 9 18	2 ×10 20
3 × 1 3	3 × 2 6	3 × 3 9	3 × 4 12	3 × 5 15	3 × 6 18	3 × 7 21	3 × 8 24	3 × 9 27	3 ×10 30
4 × 1 4	4 × 2 8	4 × 3 12	4 × 4 16	4 × 5 20	4 × 6 24	4 × 7 28	4 × 8 32	4 × 9 36	4 ×10 40
5 × 1 5	5 × 2 10	5 × 3 15	5 × 4 20	5 × 5 25	5 × 6 30	5 × 7 35	5 × 8 40	5 × 9 45	5 ×10 50
6 × 1 6	6 × 2 12	6 × 3 18	6 × 4 24	6 × 5 30	6 × 6 36	6 × 7 42	6 × 8 48	6 × 9 54	6 ×10 60
7 × 1 7	7 × 2 14	7 × 3 21	7 × 4 28	7 × 5 35	7 × 6 42	7 × 7 49	7 × 8 56	7 × 9 63	7 ×10 70
8 × 1 8	8 × 2 16	8 × 3 24	8 × 4 32	8 × 5 40	8 × 6 48	8 × 7 56	8 × 8 64	8 × 9 72	8 ×10 80
9 × 1 9	9 × 2 18	9 × 3 27	9 × 4 36	9 × 5 45	9 × 6 54	9 × 7 63	9 × 8 72	9 × 9 81	9 ×10 90
10 × 1 10	10 × 2 20	10 × 3 30	10 × 4 40	10 × 5 50	10 × 6 60	10 × 7 70	10 × 8 80	10 × 9 90	10 ×10 100

MULTIPLY

9	5	8	7	3	1	4	2	10	6
× 1	× 2	× 3	× 4	× 5	× 6	× 7	× 8	× 9	×10

8	9	6	5	10	2	1	3	4	7
× 1	× 2	× 3	× 4	× 5	× 6	× 7	× 8	× 9	×10

7	6	5	4	9	3	2	8	1	10
× 1	× 2	× 3	× 4	× 5	× 6	× 7	× 8	× 9	×10

5	8	4	6	1	9	10	7	2	3
× 1	× 2	× 3	× 4	× 5	× 6	× 7	× 8	× 9	×10

10	4	2	3	7	5	8	1	6	9
× 1	× 2	× 3	× 4	× 5	× 6	× 7	× 8	× 9	×10

6	7	10	1	4	8	9	5	3	2
× 1	× 2	× 3	× 4	× 5	× 6	× 7	× 8	× 9	×10

4	3	1	2	6	10	7	9	5	8
× 1	× 2	× 3	× 4	× 5	× 6	× 7	× 8	× 9	×10

1	2	7	9	5	6	3	10	8	4
× 1	× 2	× 3	× 4	× 5	× 6	× 7	× 8	× 9	×10

3	10	9	8	2	4	5	6	7	1
× 1	× 2	× 3	× 4	× 5	× 6	× 7	× 8	× 9	×10

2	1	3	10	8	7	6	4	9	5
× 1	× 2	× 3	× 4	× 5	× 6	× 7	× 8	× 9	×10

53

MULTIPLY BY MULTIPLES OF 10

10 × 6 —— 60	10 × 4	10 × 8	10 × 5
10 × 3	10 × 0	20 × 6	20 × 3
20 × 2	20 × 7	20 × 4	20 × 5
20 × 9	30 × 9	30 × 6	30 × 7
30 × 5	30 × 3	30 × 4	30 × 8
40 × 7	40 × 6	40 × 9	40 × 5
40 × 2	40 × 3	40 × 8	40 × 4

MULTIPLY BY MULTIPLES OF 10

50	50	50	50
× 2	× 5	× 3	× 7
100			

50	50	50	50
× 1	× 6	× 8	× 4

60	60	60	60
× 3	× 8	× 7	× 6

60	60	60	70
× 5	× 4	× 9	× 8

70	70	70	70
× 7	× 4	× 6	× 9

80	80	80	80
× 3	× 2	× 4	× 6

90	90	90	90
× 5	× 9	× 7	× 8

MULTIPLY BY MULTIPLES OF 10 AND 100

10	40	100	300
× 7	× 9	× 5	× 9
70			

10	70	200	500
× 6	× 8	× 5	× 4

20	90	900	700
× 9	× 9	× 6	× 3

30	50	400	600
× 4	× 7	× 8	× 2

60	80	700	800
× 5	× 3	× 8	× 9

40	70	500	200
× 6	× 9	× 9	× 8

90	50	100	300
× 6	× 4	× 7	× 9

MULTIPLY BY MULTIPLES OF 10 AND 100

70	90	500	600
× 4	× 7	× 8	× 6
280			

100	200	80	50
× 8	× 9	× 7	× 3

400	900	700	800
× 4	× 9	× 7	× 6

60	40	300	70
× 9	× 6	× 5	× 3

80	60	200	500
× 9	× 7	× 8	× 7

30	300	100	400
× 6	× 3	× 9	× 8

20	70	500	900
× 6	× 7	× 6	× 8

MULTIPLY BY MULTIPLES OF 100

100 × 8 800	100 × 7	100 × 6	200 × 5
200 × 4	200 × 9	300 × 8	300 × 3
300 × 7	300 × 2	400 × 9	400 × 8
400 × 6	400 × 5	500 × 7	500 × 9
500 × 8	600 × 6	600 × 9	600 × 7
700 × 9	700 × 4	700 × 8	800 × 6
800 × 3	800 × 5	900 × 6	900 × 9

MULTIPLY BY MULTIPLES OF 100

700 × 9 ── 6300	500 × 4 ──	600 × 7 ──	800 × 3 ──
400 × 5 ──	300 × 6 ──	900 × 2 ──	400 × 4 ──
200 × 8 ──	900 × 7 ──	500 × 4 ──	300 × 9 ──
100 × 5 ──	400 × 3 ──	700 × 6 ──	900 × 2 ──
800 × 6 ──	500 × 9 ──	300 × 8 ──	200 × 4 ──
600 × 7 ──	300 × 2 ──	900 × 5 ──	700 × 3 ──
500 × 4 ──	900 × 8 ──	700 × 9 ──	800 × 6 ──

FIND THE PRODUCT

3 × 2 = __6__

3 × 20 = __60__

3 × 200 = __600__

3 × 2,000 = __6,000__

5 × 5 = _____

5 × 50 = _____

5 × 500 = _____

5 × 5,000 = _____

4 × 3 = _____

4 × 30 = _____

4 × 300 = _____

4 × 3,000 = _____

6 × 3 = _____

6 × 30 = _____

6 × 300 = _____

6 × 3,000 = _____

7 × 2 = _____

7 × 20 = _____

7 × 200 = _____

7 × 2,000 = _____

8 × 4 = _____

8 × 40 = _____

8 × 400 = _____

8 × 4,000 = _____

9 × 3 = _____

9 × 30 = _____

9 × 300 = _____

9 × 3,000 = _____

6 × 6 = _____

6 × 60 = _____

6 × 600 = _____

6 × 6,000 = _____

2 × 6 = _____

2 × 60 = _____

2 × 600 = _____

2 × 6,000 = _____

4 × 4 = _____

4 × 40 = _____

4 × 400 = _____

4 × 4,000 = _____

FIND THE PRODUCT

4 × 7 = _____

4 × 70 = _____

4 × 700 = _____

4 × 7,000 = _____

8 × 9 = _____

8 × 90 = _____

8 × 900 = _____

8 × 9,000 = _____

5 × 8 = _____

5 × 80 = _____

5 × 800 = _____

5 × 8,000 = _____

7 × 5 = _____

7 × 50 = _____

7 × 500 = _____

7 × 5,000 = _____

8 × 8 = _____

8 × 80 = _____

8 × 800 = _____

8 × 8,000 = _____

8 × 6 = _____

8 × 60 = _____

8 × 600 = _____

8 × 6,000 = _____

7 × 7 = _____

7 × 70 = _____

7 × 700 = _____

7 × 7,000 = _____

6 × 9 = _____

6 × 90 = _____

6 × 900 = _____

6 × 9,000 = _____

5 × 9 = _____

5 × 90 = _____

5 × 900 = _____

5 × 9,000 = _____

9 × 4 = _____

9 × 40 = _____

9 × 400 = _____

9 × 4,000 = _____

MULTIPLY BY 1-DIGIT

47 × 1	57 × 1	36 × 1	78 × 2
86 × 2	53 × 2	48 × 3	18 × 3
58 × 3	87 × 4	85 × 4	75 × 4
63 × 5	45 × 5	83 × 5	76 × 6
89 × 6	87 × 6	73 × 7	38 × 7
82 × 7	59 × 8	53 × 8	45 × 8
25 × 9	42 × 9	23 × 9	74 × 9

MULTIPLY BY 1-DIGIT

230 × 5	519 × 4	185 × 7	306 × 6
624 × 3	450 × 7	523 × 9	473 × 2
408 × 6	278 × 5	303 × 8	624 × 7
855 × 4	789 × 3	909 × 7	643 × 8
227 × 4	126 × 1	289 × 8	559 × 2
680 × 6	472 × 9	873 × 3	994 × 5
571 × 2	389 × 6	743 × 8	408 × 7

MULTIPLY BY 2-DIGIT ★

60 ×35	70 × 29	50 × 42	40 × 33
20 ×15	30 × 28	80 × 53	90 × 62
24 ×35	42 × 43	72 × 32	54 × 28
67 ×24	58 × 62	97 × 45	83 × 37
94 ×48	62 × 35	78 × 58	59 × 66

MULTIPLY BY 2-DIGIT

153 × 24	356 × 26	253 × 28	409 × 27
628 × 35	485 × 43	547 × 55	736 × 28
362 × 42	658 × 62	425 × 37	583 × 56
155 × 25	245 × 39	308 × 44	633 × 53
526 × 63	219 × 78	448 × 27	560 × 48

DIVIDE BY 1 AND 2

5 ÷ 1 = _____

10 ÷ 1 = _____

12 ÷ 1 = _____

9 ÷ 1 = _____

2 ÷ 1 = _____

11 ÷ 1 = _____

10 ÷ 2 = _____

14 ÷ 2 = _____

18 ÷ 2 = _____

24 ÷ 2 = _____

8 ÷ 1 = _____

7 ÷ 1 = _____

4 ÷ 1 = _____

3 ÷ 1 = _____

1 ÷ 1 = _____

6 ÷ 1 = _____

2 ÷ 2 = _____

16 ÷ 2 = _____

12 ÷ 2 = _____

20 ÷ 2 = _____

quotient   divided by   average   divide   divided equally

dividend   per   each

DIVIDE BY 3 AND 4

$9 \div 3 = \underline{\hspace{1.5cm}}$ $15 \div 3 = \underline{\hspace{1.5cm}}$

$12 \div 3 = \underline{\hspace{1.5cm}}$ $6 \div 3 = \underline{\hspace{1.5cm}}$

$21 \div 3 = \underline{\hspace{1.5cm}}$ $30 \div 3 = \underline{\hspace{1.5cm}}$

$27 \div 3 = \underline{\hspace{1.5cm}}$ $3 \div 3 = \underline{\hspace{1.5cm}}$

$36 \div 3 = \underline{\hspace{1.5cm}}$ $18 \div 3 = \underline{\hspace{1.5cm}}$

$33 \div 3 = \underline{\hspace{1.5cm}}$ $12 \div 4 = \underline{\hspace{1.5cm}}$

$4 \div 4 = \underline{\hspace{1.5cm}}$ $20 \div 4 = \underline{\hspace{1.5cm}}$

$16 \div 4 = \underline{\hspace{1.5cm}}$ $24 \div 4 = \underline{\hspace{1.5cm}}$

$28 \div 4 = \underline{\hspace{1.5cm}}$ $40 \div 4 = \underline{\hspace{1.5cm}}$

$8 \div 4 = \underline{\hspace{1.5cm}}$ $32 \div 4 = \underline{\hspace{1.5cm}}$

$36 \div 4 = \underline{\hspace{1.5cm}}$ $48 \div 4 = \underline{\hspace{1.5cm}}$

67

DIVIDE BY 5 AND 6

10 ÷ 5 = _____

5 ÷ 5 = _____

20 ÷ 5 = _____

45 ÷ 5 = _____

50 ÷ 5 = _____

55 ÷ 5 = _____

6 ÷ 6 = _____

12 ÷ 6 = _____

24 ÷ 6 = _____

42 ÷ 6 = _____

60 ÷ 6= _____

25 ÷ 5 = _____

30 ÷ 5 = _____

15 ÷ 5 = _____

35 ÷ 5 = _____

40 ÷ 5 = _____

24 ÷ 6 = _____

18 ÷ 6 = _____

30 ÷ 6 = _____

36 ÷ 6 = _____

48 ÷ 6 = _____

54 ÷ 6 = _____

DIVIDE BY 7 AND 8

21 ÷ 7 = _____   14 ÷ 7 = _____

7 ÷ 7 = _____   28 ÷ 7 = _____

42 ÷ 7 = _____   56 ÷ 7 = _____

63 ÷ 7 = _____   49 ÷ 7 = _____

35 ÷ 7 = _____   70 ÷ 7 = _____

77 ÷ 7 = _____   16 ÷ 8 = _____

24 ÷ 8 = _____   8 ÷ 8 = _____

64 ÷ 8 = _____   48 ÷ 8 = _____

80 ÷ 8 = _____   40 ÷ 8 = _____

88 ÷ 8 = _____   72 ÷ 8 = _____

56 ÷ 8 = _____   32 ÷ 8 = _____

DIVIDE BY 9 AND 10

36 ÷ 9 = _____   54 ÷ 9 = _____

45 ÷ 9 = _____   18 ÷ 9 = _____

9 ÷ 9 = _____   63 ÷ 9 = _____

72 ÷ 9 = _____   90 ÷ 9 = _____

27 ÷ 9 = _____   99 ÷ 9 = _____

108 ÷ 9 = _____   10 ÷ 10 = _____

50 ÷ 10 = _____   80 ÷ 10 = _____

70 ÷ 10 = _____   40 ÷ 10 = _____

30 ÷ 10 = _____   100 ÷ 10 = _____

90 ÷ 10 = _____   20 ÷ 10 = _____

60 ÷ 10 = _____   110 ÷ 10 = _____

DIVIDE BY 11 AND 12

48 ÷ 12 = _____

60 ÷ 12 = _____

44 ÷ 11 = _____

33 ÷ 11 = _____

66 ÷ 11 = _____

72 ÷ 12 = _____

36 ÷ 12 = _____

24 ÷ 12 = _____

22 ÷ 11 = _____

11 ÷ 11 = _____

144 ÷ 12 = _____

110 ÷ 11 = _____

96 ÷ 12 = _____

108 ÷ 12 = _____

55 ÷ 11 = _____

77 ÷ 11 = _____

12 ÷ 12 = _____

84 ÷ 12 = _____

88 ÷ 11 = _____

132 ÷ 12 = _____

99 ÷ 11 = _____

132 ÷ 11 = _____

DIVIDE

8 ÷ 8 = _____

20 ÷ 4 = _____

36 ÷ 9 = _____

16 ÷ 2 = _____

12 ÷ 4 = _____

21 ÷ 3 = _____

18 ÷ 9 = _____

40 ÷ 10 = _____

32 ÷ 4 = _____

60 ÷ 6 = _____

120 ÷ 10 = _____

12 ÷ 3 = _____

14 ÷ 2 = _____

30 ÷ 5 = _____

40 ÷ 8 = _____

14 ÷ 7 = _____

30 ÷ 5= _____

25 ÷ 5 = _____

22 ÷ 11 = _____

80 ÷ 10 = _____

35 ÷ 7 = _____

84 ÷ 12 = _____

DIVIDE

16 ÷ 8 = _____

40 ÷ 5 = _____

20 ÷ 4 = _____

32 ÷ 8 = _____

18 ÷ 3 = _____

45 ÷ 9 = _____

12 ÷ 4 = _____

50 ÷ 5 = _____

70 ÷ 7 = _____

15 ÷ 3 = _____

90 ÷ 9 = _____

36 ÷ 4 = _____

63 ÷ 7 = _____

81 ÷ 9 = _____

30 ÷ 6 = _____

27 ÷ 9 = _____

60 ÷ 10 = _____

20 ÷ 2 = _____

72 ÷ 9 = _____

24 ÷ 8 = _____

49 ÷ 7 = _____

60 ÷ 12 = _____

I LOVE MATH

DIVIDE

360 ÷ 9 = _____   640 ÷ 8 = _____

720 ÷ 8 = _____   160 ÷ 4 = _____

200 ÷ 5 = _____   350 ÷ 7 = _____

450 ÷ 9 = _____   420 ÷ 6 = _____

210 ÷ 7 = _____   140 ÷ 2 = _____

240 ÷ 3 = _____   540 ÷ 6 = _____

300 ÷ 6 = _____   270 ÷ 9 = _____

600 ÷ 6 = _____   630 ÷ 7 = _____

320 ÷ 4 = _____   330 ÷ 3 = _____

240 ÷ 12 = _____   480 ÷ 8 = _____

400 ÷ 5 = _____   960 ÷ 12 = _____

DIVIDE ★

$450 \div 50 = $ _____

$360 \div 90 = $ _____

$600 \div 60 = $ _____

$320 \div 40 = $ _____

$420 \div 70 = $ _____

$400 \div 50 = $ _____

$240 \div 80 = $ _____

$450 \div 50 = $ _____

$210 \div 30 = $ _____

$560 \div 70 = $ _____

$220 \div 110 = $ _____

$720 \div 90 = $ _____

$540 \div 60 = $ _____

$480 \div 80 = $ _____

$640 \div 80 = $ _____

$180 \div 20 = $ _____

$810 \div 90 = $ _____

$630 \div 90 = $ _____

$140 \div 70 = $ _____

$200 \div 40 = $ _____

$250 \div 50 = $ _____

$480 \div 120 = $ _____

DIVISION CHART

÷ 1	÷ 2	÷ 3	÷ 4	÷ 5	÷ 6	÷ 7	÷ 8	÷ 9	÷ 10
1 ÷ 1 1	2 ÷ 2 1	3 ÷ 3 1	4 ÷ 4 1	5 ÷ 5 1	6 ÷ 6 1	7 ÷ 7 1	8 ÷ 8 1	9 ÷ 9 1	10 ÷ 10 1
2 ÷ 1 2	4 ÷ 2 2	6 ÷ 3 2	8 ÷ 4 2	10 ÷ 5 2	12 ÷ 6 2	14 ÷ 7 2	16 ÷ 8 2	18 ÷ 9 2	20 ÷ 10 2
3 ÷ 1 3	6 ÷ 2 3	9 ÷ 3 3	12 ÷ 4 3	15 ÷ 5 3	18 ÷ 6 3	21 ÷ 7 3	24 ÷ 8 3	27 ÷ 9 3	30 ÷ 10 3
4 ÷ 1 4	8 ÷ 2 4	12 ÷ 3 4	16 ÷ 4 4	20 ÷ 5 4	24 ÷ 6 4	28 ÷ 7 4	32 ÷ 8 4	36 ÷ 9 4	40 ÷ 10 4
5 ÷ 1 5	10 ÷ 2 5	15 ÷ 3 5	20 ÷ 4 5	25 ÷ 5 5	30 ÷ 6 5	35 ÷ 7 5	40 ÷ 8 5	45 ÷ 9 5	50 ÷ 10 5
6 ÷ 1 6	12 ÷ 2 6	18 ÷ 3 6	24 ÷ 4 6	30 ÷ 5 6	36 ÷ 6 6	42 ÷ 7 6	48 ÷ 8 6	54 ÷ 9 6	60 ÷ 10 6
7 ÷ 1 7	14 ÷ 2 7	21 ÷ 3 7	28 ÷ 4 7	35 ÷ 5 7	42 ÷ 6 7	49 ÷ 7 7	56 ÷ 8 7	63 ÷ 9 7	70 ÷ 10 7
8 ÷ 1 8	16 ÷ 2 8	24 ÷ 3 8	32 ÷ 4 8	40 ÷ 5 8	48 ÷ 6 8	56 ÷ 7 8	64 ÷ 8 8	72 ÷ 9 8	80 ÷ 10 8
9 ÷ 1 9	18 ÷ 2 9	27 ÷ 3 9	36 ÷ 4 9	45 ÷ 5 9	54 ÷ 6 9	63 ÷ 7 9	72 ÷ 8 9	81 ÷ 9 9	90 ÷ 10 9
10 ÷ 1 10	20 ÷ 2 10	30 ÷ 3 10	40 ÷ 4 10	50 ÷ 5 10	60 ÷ 6 10	70 ÷ 7 10	80 ÷ 8 10	90 ÷ 9 10	100 ÷ 10 10

MORE DIVISION

72 ÷ 8	6 ÷ 1	42 ÷ 7	1 ÷ 1	30 ÷ 3	54 ÷ 9	12 ÷ 4	24 ÷ 4	36 ÷ 9	20 ÷ 10
28 ÷ 4	6 ÷ 6	80 ÷ 10	45 ÷ 5	63 ÷ 9	8 ÷ 4	48 ÷ 8	36 ÷ 4	12 ÷ 3	14 ÷ 2
10 ÷ 1	14 ÷ 7	18 ÷ 3	4 ÷ 2	21 ÷ 7	30 ÷ 5	2 ÷ 2	30 ÷ 10	5 ÷ 5	80 ÷ 8
40 ÷ 4	21 ÷ 3	8 ÷ 2	24 ÷ 6	28 ÷ 7	90 ÷ 9	4 ÷ 1	12 ÷ 6	2 ÷ 1	27 ÷ 9
49 ÷ 7	9 ÷ 1	15 ÷ 5	8 ÷ 8	12 ÷ 2	27 ÷ 3	20 ÷ 5	18 ÷ 6	35 ÷ 5	40 ÷ 10
16 ÷ 8	10 ÷ 10	42 ÷ 6	72 ÷ 9	20 ÷ 2	64 ÷ 8	60 ÷ 10	50 ÷ 5	45 ÷ 9	18 ÷ 9
18 ÷ 2	32 ÷ 8	10 ÷ 5	16 ÷ 4	10 ÷ 2	3 ÷ 3	15 ÷ 3	24 ÷ 3	54 ÷ 6	48 ÷ 6
40 ÷ 5	36 ÷ 6	3 ÷ 1	63 ÷ 7	56 ÷ 8	56 ÷ 7	60 ÷ 6	20 ÷ 4	9 ÷ 9	30 ÷ 6
70 ÷ 7	16 ÷ 2	4 ÷ 4	25 ÷ 5	35 ÷ 7	6 ÷ 3	24 ÷ 8	7 ÷ 1	70 ÷ 10	81 ÷ 9

DIVISION WITH REMAINDERS

9 ÷ 4 ⭐⭐ ⭐⭐ ★ ⭐⭐ ⭐⭐ <u>2R1</u>	12 ÷ 5	15 ÷ 6	20 ÷ 3	14 ÷ 8	22 ÷ 4	28 ÷ 5	19 ÷ 7
32 ÷ 6	29 ÷ 4	61 ÷ 10	70 ÷ 8	51 ÷ 9	39 ÷ 7	43 ÷ 6	36 ÷ 5
49 ÷ 9	26 ÷ 8	34 ÷ 7	57 ÷ 9	23 ÷ 4	18 ÷ 5	65 ÷ 9	50 ÷ 6
41 ÷ 7	77 ÷ 9	53 ÷ 8	25 ÷ 6	31 ÷ 7	19 ÷ 5	44 ÷ 6	65 ÷ 9
27 ÷ 5	34 ÷ 6	71 ÷ 9	43 ÷ 5	11 ÷ 9	22 ÷ 4	29 ÷ 3	38 ÷ 6
14 ÷ 8	55 ÷ 10	58 ÷ 6	23 ÷ 9	19 ÷ 2	61 ÷ 8	73 ÷ 8	33 ÷ 7

Fact Family

Whiz Kids' Example 4 × 8 = 32 __8__ × __4__ = __32__ __32__ ÷ __4__ = __8__ __32__ ÷ __8__ = __4__	9 × 3 = 27 ___ × ___ = ___ ___ ÷ ___ = ___ ___ ÷ ___ = ___	8 × 6 = 48 ___ × ___ = ___ ___ ÷ ___ = ___ ___ ÷ ___ = ___	7 × 8 = 56 ___ × ___ = ___ ___ ÷ ___ = ___ ___ ÷ ___ = ___
6 × 9 = 54 ___ × ___ = ___ ___ ÷ ___ = ___ ___ ÷ ___ = ___	7 × 4 = 28 ___ × ___ = ___ ___ ÷ ___ = ___ ___ ÷ ___ = ___	4 × 5 = 20 ___ × ___ = ___ ___ ÷ ___ = ___ ___ ÷ ___ = ___	5 × 9 = 45 ___ × ___ = ___ ___ ÷ ___ = ___ ___ ÷ ___ = ___
3 × 8 = 24 ___ × ___ = ___ ___ ÷ ___ = ___ ___ ÷ ___ = ___	7 × 9 = 63 ___ × ___ = ___ ___ ÷ ___ = ___ ___ ÷ ___ = ___	3 × 10 = 30 ___ × ___ = ___ ___ ÷ ___ = ___ ___ ÷ ___ = ___	6 × 7 = 42 ___ × ___ = ___ ___ ÷ ___ = ___ ___ ÷ ___ = ___

Fact Family

$4 \times \boxed{8} = 32$

$\underline{8} \times \underline{4} = \underline{32}$

$\underline{32} \div \underline{4} = \underline{8}$

$\underline{32} \div \underline{8} = \underline{4}$

$8 \times \square = 40$

___ × ___ = ___

___ ÷ ___ = ___

___ ÷ ___ = ___

$9 \times \square = 36$

___ × ___ = ___

___ ÷ ___ = ___

___ ÷ ___ = ___

$6 \times \square = 60$

___ × ___ = ___

___ ÷ ___ = ___

___ ÷ ___ = ___

$\square \times 8 = 16$

___ × ___ = ___

___ ÷ ___ = ___

___ ÷ ___ = ___

$\square \times 3 = 21$

___ × ___ = ___

___ ÷ ___ = ___

___ ÷ ___ = ___

$9 \times \square = 72$

___ × ___ = ___

___ ÷ ___ = ___

___ ÷ ___ = ___

$6 \times \square = 30$

___ × ___ = ___

___ ÷ ___ = ___

___ ÷ ___ = ___

$7 \times \square = 35$

___ × ___ = ___

___ ÷ ___ = ___

___ ÷ ___ = ___

$\square \times 2 = 20$

___ × ___ = ___

___ ÷ ___ = ___

___ ÷ ___ = ___

$\square \times 10 = 80$

___ × ___ = ___

___ ÷ ___ = ___

___ ÷ ___ = ___

$\square \times 4 = 48$

___ × ___ = ___

___ ÷ ___ = ___

___ ÷ ___ = ___

Fact Family

Whiz Kids' Example	$80 \div 10 = 8$	$14 \div 2 = 7$	$21 \div 7 = 3$
$18 \div 6 = 3$ $\underline{18} \div \underline{3} = \underline{6}$ $\underline{6} \times \underline{3} = \underline{18}$ $\underline{3} \times \underline{6} = \underline{18}$	___ ÷ ___ = ___ ___ × ___ = ___ ___ × ___ = ___	___ ÷ ___ = ___ ___ × ___ = ___ ___ × ___ = ___	___ ÷ ___ = ___ ___ × ___ = ___ ___ × ___ = ___
$36 \div 9 = 4$	$60 \div 6 = 10$	$15 \div 5 = 3$	$72 \div 9 = 8$
___ ÷ ___ = ___ ___ × ___ = ___ ___ × ___ = ___	___ ÷ ___ = ___ ___ × ___ = ___ ___ × ___ = ___	___ ÷ ___ = ___ ___ × ___ = ___ ___ × ___ = ___	___ ÷ ___ = ___ ___ × ___ = ___ ___ × ___ = ___
$32 \div 4 = 8$	$12 \div 2 = 6$	$54 \div 6 = 9$	$90 \div 9 = 10$
___ ÷ ___ = ___ ___ × ___ = ___ ___ × ___ = ___	___ ÷ ___ = ___ ___ × ___ = ___ ___ × ___ = ___	___ ÷ ___ = ___ ___ × ___ = ___ ___ × ___ = ___	___ ÷ ___ = ___ ___ × ___ = ___ ___ × ___ = ___

Fact Family

$18 \div \boxed{3} = 6$

$\underline{\quad 18 \quad} \div \underline{\quad 6 \quad} = \underline{\quad 3 \quad}$

$\underline{\quad 6 \quad} \times \underline{\quad 3 \quad} = \underline{\quad 18 \quad}$

$\underline{\quad 3 \quad} \times \underline{\quad 6 \quad} = \underline{\quad 18 \quad}$

$48 \div \square = 8$

___ ÷ ___ = ___

___ × ___ = ___

___ × ___ = ___

$56 \div \square = 7$

___ ÷ ___ = ___

___ × ___ = ___

___ × ___ = ___

$\square \div 3 = 9$

___ ÷ ___ = ___

___ × ___ = ___

___ × ___ = ___

$21 \div \square = 3$

___ ÷ ___ = ___

___ × ___ = ___

___ × ___ = ___

$63 \div \square = 9$

___ ÷ ___ = ___

___ × ___ = ___

___ × ___ = ___

$\square \div 5 = 4$

___ ÷ ___ = ___

___ × ___ = ___

___ × ___ = ___

$\square \div 9 = 8$

___ ÷ ___ = ___

___ × ___ = ___

___ × ___ = ___

$30 \div \square = 6$

___ ÷ ___ = ___

___ × ___ = ___

___ × ___ = ___

$24 \div \square = 8$

___ ÷ ___ = ___

___ × ___ = ___

___ × ___ = ___

$\square \div 8 = 10$

___ ÷ ___ = ___

___ × ___ = ___

___ × ___ = ___

$\square \div 4 = 12$

___ ÷ ___ = ___

___ × ___ = ___

___ × ___ = ___

Rounding Rules

Let's round 327 to the nearest ten.

Caleb's rules for rounding	Example
Circle the digit in the place you are rounding.	3②7 (Since we are rounding to the nearest ten, we will circle the 2; the two is in the tens place)
Then underline the digit to the righthand side of the circled digit.	3②7̲ (The 7 follows the number in the tens place; this number determines what we will do with the 2 in the tens place.)
If the underlined digit is 0-4 (0,1,2,3,4), the circled (rounding) number stays the same; all numbers to the righthand side of the circled digit become zero. OR If the underlined digit is 5-9 (5, 6, 7, 8, or 9), the circled number round up by one number; all numbers to the righthand side of the circled digit become zero.	3②7̲ 7 is NOT between 0-4, so the number 2 in the tens place does not stay the same. 3②7̲ Since 7 is between the numbers 5-9, the number 2 rounds up by one number. The number to the righthand side becomes zero. 3 0 3②7̲ = 330

Round to the nearest 10

Whiz Kids' Example	30　　40	20　　30	10　　20
20　　(30)	32	29	13
②8̲			

60　　70	40　　50	90　　100	50　　60
65	43	94	57

70　　80	80　　90	30　　40	10　　20
77	85	33	18

Round to the nearest 10

Whiz Kids' Example 420　　　　(430) 4 (2) 6	560　　　　570 568	200　　　　210 209	310　　　　320 314
780　　　　790 783	100　　　　110 104	690　　　　700 694	910　　　　920 915
970　　　　980 977	620　　　　630 625	430　　　　440 434	820　　　　830 823

Round to the nearest 10

Whiz Kids' Example 580　　（590） 5 (8) 5	730　　　740 736	910　　　920 919	440　　　450 442
650　　　660 655	920　　　930 924	110　　　120 115	240　　　250 247
330　　　340 333	980　　　990 984	500　　　510 505	710　　　720 715

86

Round to the nearest 100

500 — 600	700 — 800	800 — 900	600 — 700
5 3 7	746	853	692

400 — 500	200 — 300	600 — 700	100 — 200
442	287	639	149

300 — 400	100 — 200	500 — 600	900 — 1,000
350	177	548	958

Round to the nearest 100

Whiz Kids' Example		
(600) 700	800 900	700 800	700 800
(6)19	849	750	743

600 700	800 900	400 500	600 700
672	838	451	626

800 900	300 400	500 600	800 900
855	379	544	888

88

Round to the nearest 1000 ★

Whiz Kids' Example		
(6,000) 7,000	2,000 3,000	7,000 8,000	6,000 7,000
6,230	2,499	7,545	6,399
5,000 6,000	1,000 2,000	7,000 8,000	6,000 7,000
5,500	1,359	7,279	6,533
3,000 4,000	1,000 2,000	9,000 10,000	8,000 9,000
3,496	1,500	9,448	8,825

Round to the nearest 1000 ★

Whiz Kids' Example 7,000 (8,000) 7,530	1,000 2,000 1,492	6,000 7,000 6,520	3,000 4,000 3,385
6,000 7,000 6,501	2,000 3,000 2,398	4,000 5,000 4,401	6,000 7,000 6,607
15,000 16,000 15,620	14,000 15,000 14,298	17,000 18,000 17,329	14,000 15,000 14,510

WORD SEARCH I

```
c e o s b o d i f b v y n o x e i b o z
i r s u u t w s p y q o m p a b c f r v
u h m a t b b j j l b i z l e z y h s t
m f t h e z t s t o t a l u c f i b u q
b e f c l r r r l z o c s n i r d b f
x m z m f c c u a e c s h l e z b f t f
u r i x z x e e y c e y x x r k j n r l
a o d y h j a y d r t m x y e k a b a m
d k q w m q u k j o y o a x f v m l c a
y z a d i r t v q x y r n d f y t s t a
i e h y e p h n k l b s x m i e s j i v
a n b r p h h k t e r y n x d e q o o d
f t c x d i u a e l h g j k l v x w n e
z b z r f l a d d i t i o n y p z h z z
a g p q e n r e i g q m y f j p v e y y
t e n g p a o x p d n d j r j v t t x r
t j d c o j s m i n u s z l r n v t m y
n d w r u y j e b u l n w y r j e u e x
a g e w l p w r w a i p c e l n s c a i
m o h w h f l g z q j t h r c r e q e t
```

MATH WORDS

add
addition
increase
plus

sum
total
decrease
difference

less
minus
subtract
subtraction

WORD SEARCH 2

```
l z b v x d u r m g d j j a d w u i q t
h l n z w l g a e n v t f a v n m b y k
v y e l y b z c e d b k j f o w g v q f
p i b c d y s h q r n y g d i v i d e r
t k c e h n a a u v q i u r m m d b v l
h h c y p r g i o d k e a j p i g c d m
g t o a t i w u t n e b c m v p v a b f
t o h b g n t v i e e a o i e c a u m q
t k u z x c f w e d z h s v n r m u j p
k s v b x m t i n d k o n o i b l j p q
d i v i s i o n t a r u c s f d d v d l
b n e c i v i e c f j e y p i x e v b d
i d p a q f n m n a k u i r n q t v s u
o m r i m a f v u c l r b o x t l e j q
a x w d v c n q a l g y z d a r m m q o
r y p t q t m c j z t q n u f i q h b m
m z f w w k f p x q r i w c t t v i l r
r d i v i d e n d h q w p t w b h v z s
i r b k f z e e y v q m n l k f d f k k
n o i t a c i l p i t l u m y c q s j a
```

MATH WORDS

addend
divide
dividend
division

divisor
multiplication
multiply
product

quotient
remainder
subtrahend
times

92

WORD SEARCH 3

```
r x y v f w g r d a q v q o p i e b p l
k n i t g e q w p e u j a t e e w e q a
h e s i e x k i k x c h y d h o s e y r
a s q r y j w s x j u o o r c y l h l g
p b i p f i u y b r t p m r a h t y c e
n k e t f h p x p m u x g p p g o y g r
h o f e w e r y y w q y h s o i q w z j
z w y k u f z y h z l b a s a s n e v h
e a i h g y b z o a j b x l e g e s f d
s r d y w k u v u c o m p o s e f y e w
d h e j n s c q e c u u u e n v z r w u
d q o l t z e n g e s f n u s w j p e p
g r j r l h z u q c x e a h x c k s y o
l e s s t a h z e j q z p m p m t m t v
x z d w d e t k a f m k o p v r q d f s
w m c l a m r x v v z r e o o y t n c v
c o w s g p g d g x e t j s l u v g h q
l s p n f q s j u b s c t f y k w c p b
v t u q v t e f t s p h b t k l k r n w
v x a h u v b z h p d g a c e h f t p g
```

MATH WORDS

compose
decompose
equal
fewer

fewest
larger
less
more

most
shorter
sort
taller

CERTIFICATE OF EXCELLENCE

THIS CERTIFICATE IS AWARDED TO

_____

for successfully completing Math Fact Fluency & More. You are officially a member of Caleb's Math Whiz Club!

Congratulations!

Ollie Wheeler

_____

Ollie Wheeler
President

Made in the USA
Columbia, SC
27 January 2022

54871930R00053